THIS BOOK
BELONGS TO

- - - - - - - - - - - - - -

LADYBIRD BOOKS

UK | USA | Canada | Ireland | Australia
India | New Zealand | South Africa
Ladybird Books is part of the Penguin Random House group of companies
whose addresses can be found at global.penguinrandomhouse.com.

www.penguin.co.uk    www.puffin.co.uk    www.ladybird.co.uk

Penguin
Random House
UK

First published 2019
001

Text and illustrations copyright © 9 Story Media Group Inc., 2019
Written by Cara J Stevens

#661544

Printed in China
A CIP catalogue record for this book is available from the British Library

ISBN: 978–0–241–38512–8

All correspondence to:
Ladybird Books
Penguin Random House Children's
80 Strand, London WC2R 0RL

Penguin Random House is committed to a
sustainable future for our business, our readers
and our planet. This book is made from Forest
Stewardship Council® certified paper.

# CONTENTS

# MEET THE CADETS

The cadets at Top Wing Academy are ready to earn their wings! They flock together on high-flying missions to learn new skills and become official rescue flyers.

## SWIFT

Trouble in the sky? *Swift is your guy!* Swift is a blue jay, and the unofficial leader of *Team Top Wing*. He loves racing, doing tricks and twirling through the air to show off his skills.

His goal is to be the fastest in the sky, whether he's *piloting his Flash Wing* or soaring the skies using his own wing power.

*Swift's the name – SPEED's the game!*

## PENNY

Penny the penguin is an *underwater expert* who impresses everyone with her brain power and her super-fast belly slides. She may be the smallest cadet, but she has no trouble keeping up and often arrives just in time to *save the day*.

She loves *'flying' underwater*, building up her collection of fish photos and cooling off after a good day of training in a bath full of ice cubes.

*Just chillin' and krillin'!*

Extremo-primo!

# BRODY

Brody is always ready to **splash into action** or cruise the waves. He's a laid-back puffin who can pilot anything that **zooms over the water.**

In true surfer-dude style, Brody never worries too much about making a plan – he's happy just **winging it**! The only thing that makes him happier than being on the beach or in the water is being wrapped in a group wing hug.

# ROD

Rod is an **ever-ready rooster** with a need for speed. When he takes to the streets in his **Road Wing**, Rod can really shake a tail feather no matter the terrain or the weather!

Off the road, he's a **bundle of fun and energy**, charming the crowds with his silly jokes and his corny sense of humour. Rod would do anything for his friends and he always tries his best.

Let's cock-a-doodle DO this!

# RESCUE VEHICLES

## ROAD WING
An all-terrain car with turbo boosters for super-speed.

## SPLASH WING
This slick speedboat zooms across the waves.

## FLASH WING
This supersonic jet is equipped with grabber talons for high-flying rescues.

## AQUA WING
Under water, this super submarine can really zoom!

**Draw lines to match each character with their rescue vehicle.**

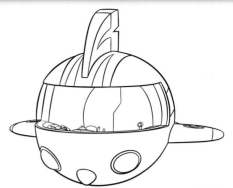

Colour in the Aqua Wing **PINK**.

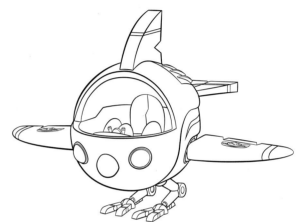

Colour in the Flash Wing **ORANGE**.

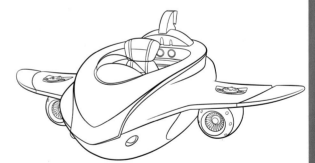

Colour in the Splash Wing **GREEN**.

Colour in the Road Wing **RED**.

# BIG SWIRL ISLAND

Big Swirl Island is home to Top Wing Academy, where the cadets learn what it takes to become rescue birds. When the cadets aren't earning badges or performing rescue missions, they can be found chilling at the Lemon Shack with their friends.

**Can you find and circle these items in the big picture?**

**PART ONE**

Swift, Brody, Penny and Rod make a great team. They met on their very first day as cadets at Top Wing Academy.

On his first day at the academy, Swift flew to Big Swirl Island. "Team Top Wing, here I come!" he said.

"Look at him go!" Speedy said to Bea as they watched him land by the two cheeky chicks, Cheep and Chirp. "That little guy can really fly!"

Swift couldn't believe how awesome the academy was. "This place is the coolest!" he said.

Penny was already there, chilling in a tub of ice. "Are you Swift?" she asked.

" Speedy says you're the best trick flyer he's ever seen. I flew here, too. Underwater," said Penny.

" Penny is a new Top Wing cadet, too," Speedy explained to Swift. "She is earning her wings as an underwater-rescue expert."

Brody was the next to arrive. He surfed in through the entrance with a loud "Akaw!"

When Rod arrived, the team was complete. "Hi! I'm Rod," he said. "How's everyone cock-a-doodle doing?"

Then Speedy welcomed the cadets to Top Wing Academy. " Bea and I think you could have what it takes to become the best rescue team ever!" he said. "At Top Wing Academy, you'll learn a lot of new skills. And each time you do, you'll earn a special badge."

Head to page 34 to find out what happens next.

# INTRODUCING . . .
# SPEEDY AND BEA

**SPEEDY** is the instructor at Top Wing Academy. **BEA** is the mechanic. She invents vehicles, fixes them and adds a little vroom when it's needed, too. Together, Speedy and Bea assign missions, guide the cadets to make good choices and award the team badges when they earn them.

Chirp and Cheep have scattered Bea's tools all over the island! Help Bea collect her tools and find her way back to Top Wing Headquarters.

Start

## MISSING LETTERS

Did you find all of Bea's tools? Fill in the missing letters to complete the name of each one.

_AMMER

T_RCH

DR_LL

SCREW_RIVER

WR_NCH

Finish

Answers on page 58.

15

GO
BANANAS!

Bananas are a tasty treat. They're good for you, too! Rhonda Rhino likes to mix them in a super smoothie with other fruit. Penny likes them mashed and frozen into an icy treat. Brody just likes to eat them plain. Do you like bananas, too?

Colour in all the bananas in this picture.

How many bananas did you colour in? Write the correct number here!

Answer on page 58.

# BEACH BABIES

The cadets are watching baby sea turtles hatch. How many turtles can you see? Write your answer here.

Draw circles around all the seashells you can see.

Look at these five objects. Can you spot them all in the big picture?

Answers on page 58.

# SURF'S UP!

When Brody's not zooming around in his super Splash Wing, he's riding the waves on his Turbo-Surfboard. Can you spot the odd one out in the pictures below?

**1**

**2**

**3**

## RIDDLE

What NEVER SAYS hello or goodbye, but always has time for a FRIENDLY WAVE?

**Answers on page 58.**

All done? Why not colour in this picture of Brody? Akaw!

# RHONDA'S
## HONEY AND CHILLI
## SUNFLOWER SEEDS

**!**

ADULT
SUPERVISION
NEEDED

*Rhonda loves making these seeds for the cadets – and now you can make them, too! Ask a grown-up to help you bake this tasty snack.*

## HERE'S HOW YOU DO IT:

**1** Preheat oven to 150°C (or fan 130°C, or gas mark 2).

**2** Place parchment paper on a baking tray. Lightly grease the paper with butter and set it aside.

**3** Mix the melted butter, honey and brown sugar together.

**4** Add the chilli powder, cinnamon, salt and seeds, then mix to coat the seeds evenly.

**5** Spread the seasoned seeds in a single layer on the greased paper.

### WHAT YOU WILL NEED:

- *Parchment paper*
- *1 tablespoon melted butter*
  *(plus extra butter for greasing)*
- *4 tablespoons honey*
- *1 tablespoon brown sugar*
- *1 teaspoon chilli powder*
  *(optional)*
- *½ teaspoon cinnamon*
  *(optional)*
- *¼ teaspoon salt*
- *280g raw sunflower seeds*
  *(or 260g raw pumpkin seeds)*

### AFTER BAKING:
- *¼ teaspoon salt*
- *½ teaspoon*
- *white sugar*

Don't like sunflower seeds? No problem! Use pumpkin seeds instead!

**6** Place the tray in the centre of the oven and bake for ten minutes.

**7** Take the tray from the oven and flip the seeds over, spreading them out again.

**8** Return the tray to the oven for ten more minutes.

**9** When you remove the seeds from the oven they should be nicely browned on both sides. Transfer the seeds to a bowl and toss them with the salt and white sugar before they cool.

**10** Spread the seeds out on the baking sheet again, and allow to cool completely before breaking them up into tasty pieces and serving.

Colour in this great pic of Rhonda!

# ROD'S BIRTHDAY SURPRISE

It's Rod's birthday! Rhonda has baked an extra-special banana cake. Brody and Penny helped by keeping Rod busy while Speedy and Bea got the party ready. Can you spot six differences between these pictures?

Colour in a badge each time you spot a difference.

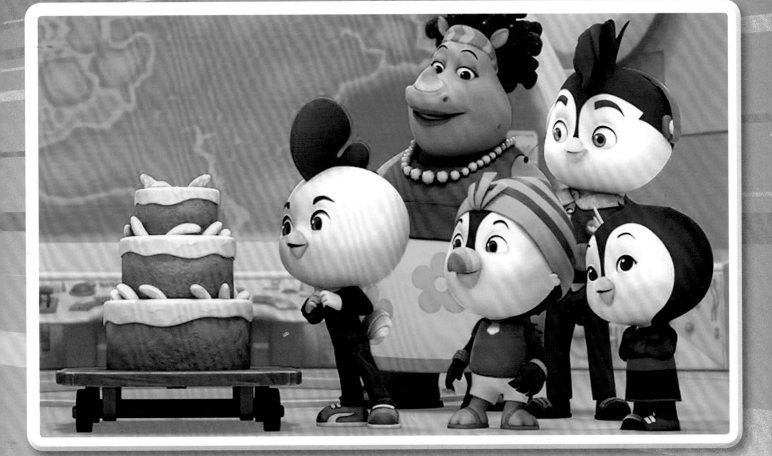

Answers on page 58.

23

# LEMON PIRATES

Cap'n Dilly and Matilda have stolen the island's lemons! Good thing Team Top Wing is on the case! Follow along with the story using your finger.

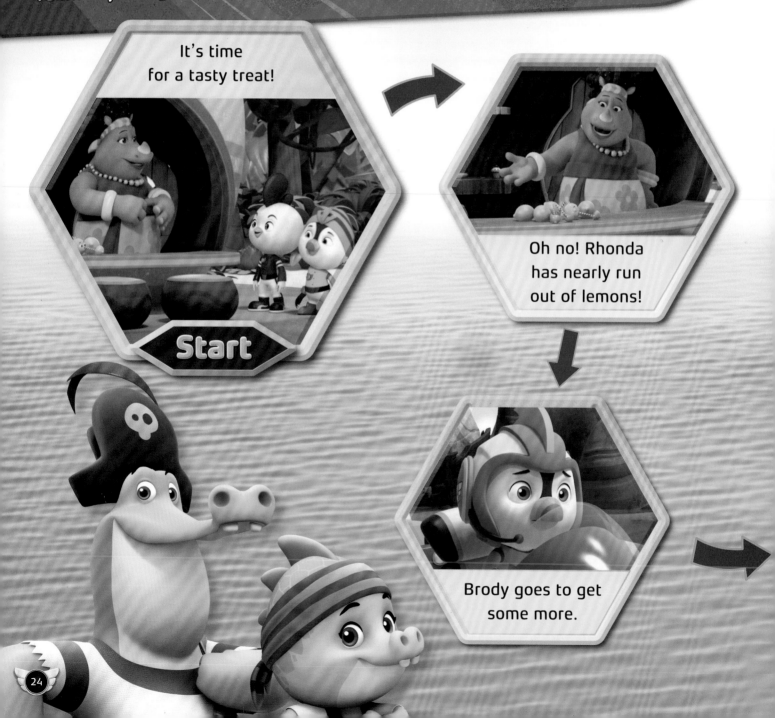

It's time for a tasty treat!

**Start**

Oh no! Rhonda has nearly run out of lemons!

Brody goes to get some more.

24

Swift and Rod rescue the lemons from Cap'n Dilly.

Brody's Splash Wing breaks down before he can rescue the lemons!

A frozen Lemon Swirly is a tasty treasure for thirsty pirates.

Rhonda makes everyone ice-cold Lemon Swirlies! Even Cap'n Dilly and Matilda.

**Finish**

Oh no! Cap'n Dilly and Matilda are stealing the lemons!

Write the word 'AHOY!' here, just like a real pirate!

AHOY!

# INTRODUCING . . .
# CHIRP
## AND
# CHEEP

Chirp and Cheep are adorable twin baby chicks who love to help out around Top Wing Academy . . . even if their help sometimes turns into another problem for the cadets to solve! They are cute, curious and lots of trouble!

Chirp and Cheep are having a play date. Can you find them in the crowd? Draw a circle around Chirp and Cheep when you find them both!

**Chirp**

**Cheep**

Answers on page 58.

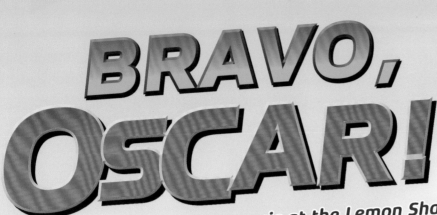

Oscar the octopus plays music at the Lemon Shack. He can play a bunch of different instruments at the same time with his awesome tentacles!

Join the dots, then colour in your picture of Oscar.

# RHYME TIME

Each of these rhymes is about a different cadet! Write the cadet's letter under the correct rhyme.

**A**

Swift

**B**

Rod

**C**

Penny

**D**

Brody

1. This boat-loving puffin lives to ride the waves,
Catching the surf is what he craves.

2. Her submarine dives deep in the sea,
Any guesses who this cool penguin could be?

3. He soars over mountains in his Flash Wing jet,
This blue jay is a super-fast cadet!

4. His Road Wing roadster is totally kickin',
But make no mistake, he's no chicken.

Answers on page 58.

# SHADOW MATCH

Only one of the shadows below matches this picture of Penny. Can you work out which one it is?

**A**    **B**    **C**    **D**    **E**

*How many seashells can you count on this page?*

Answer on page 59.

# HATCH DAY

Oh no! Sandy Stork has lost her glasses and got her egg delivery wrong. Read the clues, then draw lines to connect the eggs to the right parents.

**Mother Goose** is waiting for one egg.

**Commodore Smurkturkski's** eggs are golden.

**Mrs Turtle's** eggs have spots on them.

Answers on page 59.

Look closely at this picture of Sandy Stork delivering eggs to the folks on Big Swirl Island. Then, cover up the picture and see if you can answer these questions!

**1** Which cadet is missing from the picture?

**2** What colours are on Sandy Stork's plane?

**3** What is Rod doing with his arms?

Draw a cool pattern on this egg!

# CADET PROFILE: ROD

**ROD** is a cock-a-doodle CAN-DO rooster who zooms across Big Swirl Island in his Road Wing.

## DID YOU KNOW?

- Rod loves a good joke.
- He doesn't like getting wet.
- He can only fly a little bit.
- He really likes to dance.

"Let's **cock-a-doodle DO** this!"

"I'm a **ROOSTER,** not a chicken!"

"I was born for this **MISSION.**"

Find your way through the maze to help Rod reach his Road Wing.

"Let's BOOGIE!"

START

Answer on page 59.

. . . continued from page 13.

## PART TWO

"OK, Team Top Wing. Ready to check out your rides?" Bea asked, loading up the academy's virtual-reality projector to show each of the cadets their personal vehicle.

"Penny, your Aqua Wing will really fly . . . underwater," Bea said.

Penny looked at the slick pink submarine and couldn't believe her eyes. "That's mine? It's so cool!"

Next, Bea showed Brody his Splash Wing. He was so excited, he barely had the words to describe it. "That's so *whoosshhh-splosh*!" he said, making splashing sounds.

Bea revealed Rod's red Road Wing. "Here's your Road Wing, Rod. Complete with turbo thrusters!"

"Oh yeah, high feathers!" called out Rod, high-fiving Swift.

Finally, Bea pulled up an image of Swift's Flash Wing. "Is that my jet? Whoa!" Swift was super impressed.

"The Flash Wing will fly higher and faster than you've ever flown before," Bea explained.

"OK, cadets," said Speedy. "It's time to take wing. Are you ready to fly?"

Head to page 48 to find out what happens next.

# PENNY'S PICTURE PUZZLE

Two pieces are missing from Penny's favourite picture of her and the other cadets. Can you work out which pieces she needs to complete her photo?

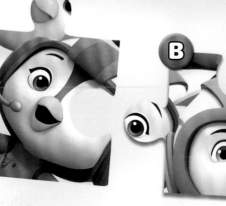

A

B

C

D

**Answers on page 59.**

# BANANA BANDITS

The banana bandits have made quite a mess on the road with their trail of banana peels! Help Rod decide which trail to follow to catch those cheeky monkeys yellow-handed.

1

2

3

Answer on page 59.

# MAKING MUSIC

When Oscar isn't helping out at the Lemon Shack, he loves to make music. Look at the musical patterns below. What colour should each white note be to finish each pattern? Use your pens to colour in each note with the correct colour.

**1**

**2**

**3**

Answers on page 59.

# SHAPE UP!

**Look at this busy scene, then complete the challenge below.**

**Draw CIRCLES** around every coconut.

**Draw SQUARES** around every honey cake.

**Draw a RECTANGLE** around Chirp and Cheep.

**Draw TRIANGLES** around every kelpsicle.

# CADET PROFILE: PENNY

**PENNY** is a penguin who pilots her underwater Aqua Wing like a pro.

## DID YOU KNOW?

- Krillsicles and Krill Icers are Penny's favourite treats.
- Penny is the youngest cadet at Top Wing Academy.
- Penny takes great pictures with her underwater camera.
- Super-fast belly slides are Penny's specialty.

*"Belly SLIDE!"*

*"Just CHILLIN' and KRILLIN'"*

*"Birds of a feather CHILL OUT together."*

Use the
number guides to
colour in your very
own picture
of Penny!

1 2 3 4 5 6

# SPOT THE DIFFERENCE

Can you find six differences between these two pictures? Each time you find one, put a tick in the badges.

Answers on page 59.

# PENNY TO THE RESCUE!

Cap'n Dilly and Matilda have stolen Greenbeard's lost treasure! It's up to Penny to rescue the treasure chest. Can you help her find her way through Shipwreck Cove to the loot?

Answers on page 59.

# CADET PROFILE: SWIFT

**SWIFT** pilots the Flash Wing – a supersonic jet equipped with grabber talons for high-flying rescues.

## DID YOU KNOW?

- Swift is the oldest cadet at Top Wing Academy.

- He loves to race and do amazing flying tricks.

- Rhonda's honey and chilli sunflower seeds are one of Swift's favourite treats.

- He prides himself on being brave and daring.

"Time to earn our WINGS!"

"Hold on to your TAIL FEATHERS!"

SWIFT'S name begins with the letter 'S'. Put a tick next to all the things below that also start with the letter 'S'!

**1**

**2**

**3**

**4**

**5**

**6**

**7**

"SWIFT's the name – SPEED's the game!"

"AWESOME!"

Answers on page 59.

47

# TIME TO EARN OUR WINGS!

. . . continued from page 35.

## PART THREE

Swift was excited for the cadets' first mission. It was in a brand new Virtual Reality Trainer that they controlled like a video game. Speedy and Bea would be watching and coaching them through the whole thing.

Their mission was to rescue a teddy bear in a boat before it went over the edge of a waterfall.

"No problem – I've got this!" said Swift, and he took off. So did Brody and Rod.

But Penny was worried. "Wait!" she cried. "If we're a team, we should work together." But it was too late. Swift, Brody and Rod had crashed! Penny used her suction grabber to reel the boat towards safety but, before it reached the riverbank, the bear slipped out of the boat and floated straight for the falls!

Rod jumped in after the bear, but then he needed to be rescued, too! Swift tried to grab Rod and the bear, but he missed. Rod and the bear went over the edge.

"End of training mission," Speedy announced. The cadets came out of their control pods feeling excited, but they were disappointed not to have succeeded.

Swift started to talk. "If that were a real rescue mission, Rod would be . . ."

". . . a very wet rooster!" said Rod, finishing Swift's sentence with a laugh.

Everyone laughed along with him. "We'll do better next time," Penny said.

But the cadets didn't have long to wait before their next mission . . . a real rescue!

Head to page 54 for the final part of your Top Wing story!

# RACE TO THE FINISH!

BRODY — 2 · 6

PENNY — 5 · 2

SWIFT — 3 · 5

ROD — 4 · 2

The cadets are having a race. Add up the number of minutes taken by each cadet to finish the race, then write their final scores in the boxes to work out who won. The cadet with the lowest score wins!

3 + 5 = ☐

1 + 3 = ☐

4 + 2 = ☐

5 + 3 = ☐

**Answers on page 59.**

# CADET PROFILE: BRODY

**BRODY** loves to make waves, zooming over the water in his Splash Wing or hanging ten on his Turbo-Surfboard.

"AKAW!"

## DID YOU KNOW?

- A group wing hug always makes Brody's day special.
- Brody loves hanging out at the beach.
- He wears a shell necklace and sandals when he isn't suited up for a mission.
- Brody's favourite colour is green.

"Primo!"

"I'm RIGHT behind YOU!"

"Guess we're just gonna have to WING IT!"

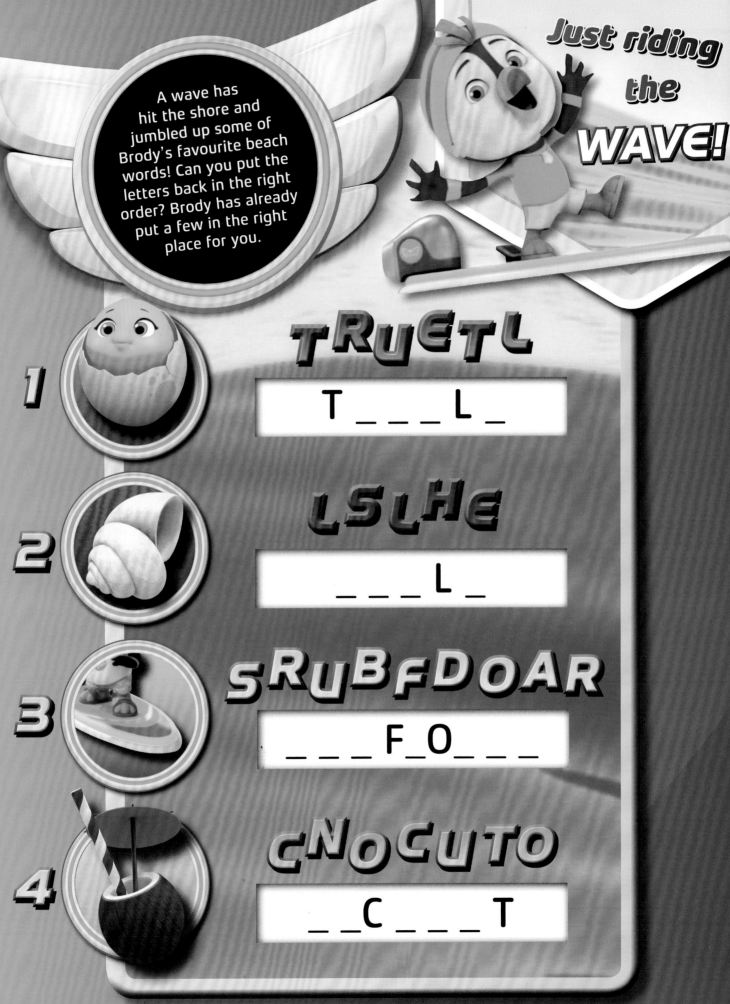

Just riding the WAVE!

A wave has hit the shore and jumbled up some of Brody's favourite beach words! Can you put the letters back in the right order? Brody has already put a few in the right place for you.

1. TRuETL

T _ _ _ L _

2. LSLHE

_ _ _ L _

3. SRuBFDOAR

_ _ _ F _ O _ _ _

4. cNoCuTO

_ _ C _ _ _ T

. . . continued from page 49.

## PART FOUR

Bea led the cadets to her workshop. "This is where I put the *vroom vroom* in your rescue rides."

"Wow!" called Brody, looking at his Splash Wing. "This speedboat is so rad!"

Cheep and Chirp thought so, too. The two chicks hopped into the speedboat, jumping up and down on the control panel. Their jumping started the speedboat and it took off with Cheep and Chirp inside . . . and no one to steer!

"What are we going to do?" asked Brody. Speedy sounded the emergency alarm. "I know just the cadets for this mission," he said. "Team Top Wing!"

Rod wasn't sure they were ready, but Swift was feeling confident. "We can do this!" he said. "We just need to make a flight plan and work as a team."

The team hopped into their vehicles . . . all except Brody. His Splash Wing was out on the water with Cheep and Chirp. He hopped on a Turbo-Surfboard and joined the rest of the team. "Akaw!"

The Splash Wing was out of control and zooming towards the waterfall – just like in the training mission! But this time the cadets were ready. Rod launched a grabber to take hold of the speedboat, then Brody hopped on board with the chicks, taking back control of the Splash Wing. Penny retrieved Brody's Turbo-Surfboard and it looked like mission complete . . . until Brody's Splash Wing lost power. It was headed straight for the falls!

Swift grabbed the speedboat using the talons on the bottom of his Flash Wing. He made it just in time!

"Nice work, Team Top Wing!" Speedy said when Cheep and Chirp and the cadets returned to base. "Bea and I are proud to award you your first badges!"

"That's so cool!" Penny said.

"You're going to be a great rescue team," said Bea.

"I think we already are," Swift said proudly.

## THE END

# QUIZ TIME!

Can you remember what happened in the story 'Time to Earn Our Wings!'? It's time to put your memory to the test! AKAW!

**1** What did Team Top Wing have to rescue in their first virtual mission?

**A** An egg

**B** A teddy bear

**C** The Turbo-Surfboard

**2** What vehicle does Penny drive?

**A** The Penny Special

**B** The Aqua Wing

**C** The Super Special Sub

**3** Who accidentally started Brody's Splash Wing?

**A** Chirp and Cheep

**B** Shirley

**C** Matilda

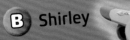

**4** Who drives the Road Wing?

**A** Rod

**B** Chirp

**C** Brody

56

**Answers on page 59.**

**5** What did Team Top Wing earn when they completed their mission?

(A) A trophy

(B) A flag

(C) A badge

**6** What did Brody ride to help rescue his runaway Splash Wing?

(A) Shirley's plane

(B) A skateboard

(C)

**YOU DID IT!** You're an honorary cadet! Draw yourself into this awesome picture.

# ANSWERS

Page 9
**RESCUE VEHICLES**

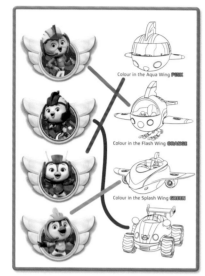

Pages 10–11
**BIG SWIRL ISLAND**

Pages 14–15
**INTRODUCING . . . SPEEDY AND BEA**

**HAMMER TORCH DRILL
SCREWDRIVER WRENCH**

Pages 16–17
**GO BANANAS!**
There are five bananas to colour in.

Page 18
**BEACH BABIES**
There are seven hatched baby turtles
and four seashells.

Page 19
**SURF'S UP!**
Number 1 is the odd one out – Brody's
shirt is missing its logo.
RIDDLE: The sea!

Pages 22–23
**ROD'S BIRTHDAY SURPRISE**

Page 26
**INTRODUCING . . . CHIRP AND CHEEP**

Page 28
**RHYME TIME**
1. D, 2. C, 3. A, 4. B

## Page 29
### SHADOW MATCH
The correct shadow is D.
There are eight seashells on the page.

## Page 30
### HATCH DAY

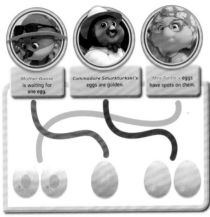

## Page 33
### CADET PROFILE: ROD

## Page 36
### PENNY'S PICTURE PUZZLE
Puzzle pieces B and C are needed to complete the photo.

## Page 37
### BANANA BANDITS
Trail 3 will lead Rod to the monkeys.

## Page 38
### MAKING MUSIC

## Pages 42–43
### SPOT THE DIFFERENCE

## Pages 44–45
### PENNY TO THE RESCUE!

## Page 47
### CADET PROFILE: SWIFT
These things start with 'S'
1. SHELL
3. SIGN
4. SKATEBOARD
7. SCREWDRIVER

## Pages 50–51
### RACE TO THE FINISH!
The winner is Penny, who was the fastest with 11 minutes.

## Page 53
### CADET PROFILE: BRODY
1. TURTLE, 2. SHELL,
3. SURFBOARD, 4. COCONUT

## Pages 56–57
### QUIZ TIME!
1. B, 2. B, 3. A, 4. A, 5. C, 6. C

# GO, TEAM TOP WING!